Max ____

Concerto No. 1 for Violin and Orchestra in G minor / g-Moll

Op. 26

Edited by / Herausgegeben von
Richard Clarke

EULENBURG

EAS 118
ISBN 978-3-7957-6518-7
ISMN M-2002-2341-5

© 2007 Ernst Eulenburg & Co GmbH, Mainz
for Europe excluding the British Isles
Ernst Eulenburg Ltd, London
for all other countries
Edition based on Eulenburg Study Score ETP 714
CD ℗ & © 1989 Naxos Rights International Ltd

Ernst Eulenburg Ltd
48 Great Marlborough Street
London W1F 7BB

Contents / Inhalt

Preface

Composed: 1864–1868 in Cologne
First performance: Koblenz, 24 April 1866; Soloist: Otto von Königslöw;
conducted by Max Bruch
First performance of the revised version: Bremen, 7 January 1868;
Soloist: Joseph Joachim; conducted by Max Bruch
Original publisher: Simrock, Berlin, 1872
Instrumentation: 2 Flutes, 2 Oboes, 2 Clarinets, 2 Bassoons –
4 Horns, 2 Trumpets – Timpani – Strings
Duration: ca. 24 minutes

Max Bruch (1838–1920) received his earliest musical training from his mother who was a well-known singer and music teacher. In 1852, at the age of 14, he won the Frankfurt Mozart Foundation Prize, which allowed him to study composition with Hiller and piano with Reinecke in Cologne. Bruch subsequently enjoyed a considerable reputation as both a conductor and a composer. He travelled extensively in Europe and was, for a time, conductor of the Liverpool Philharmonic Orchestra, later accepting a similar appointment in Breslau. In 1891 he was appointed to direct a master-class in composition at the Musikhochschule in Berlin.

Although it is not Bruch's only instrumental concerto, his G minor Violin Concerto remains his best-known piece and continues to enjoy wide popularity among performers and audiences alike. The enduring popularity of the concerto lies perhaps in its appealing mixture of romantic sentiment (especially in the *Adagio*) and in its exuberant, virtuosic instrumental display throughout. That Bruch took great care in deciding on the final shape of the work is apparent from his remarks to Simrock written in 1872: 'Between 1864 and 1868 I rewrote my concerto at least a half dozen times, and conferred with x violinists before it achieved its final form'.

The correspondence between Bruch and Joachim that survives from the period of the work's revision, gives us some valuable insight into the working partnership of composer and eventual soloist, even down to details of the work's generic description and final title. Bruch was evidently unsure about describing the work as a concerto at all, as we learn from this subtle and sympathetic response from the great violinist: 'As to your doubts', writes Joachim, 'I am happy to say that I find the title "concerto" fully justified; the last two movements are too completely and symmetrically developed to justify the name "fantasy"'.

The concerto somewhat radically and unexpectedly, however, avoids traditional forms. The first movement is a rhapsodic prelude to the whole work and opens with a quasi-improvisatory arpeggio flourish for the soloist. The second, contrasting theme in B flat major, is again introduced by the soloist, and consists of a long cantabile melody that slowly ascends through the violin's register with a succession of trill figures. The work then proceeds in a more-or-less standard sonata-form pattern. The themes, having thus been announced, are subjected to a series of developments until – instead of a traditional recapitulation – the opening violin arpeggio figures return and provide instead a transition leading without a break to the second movement, the emotional and thematic core of the work.

The central *Adagio* movement – in the contrasting key of E flat major – opens with a violin melody of great emotional intensity. The movement unfolds a succession of themes, the first three of which are introduced by the soloist. A fourth theme is announced by the horns and woodwind against a highly-decorated triplet figure played by the soloist. The *Adagio* concludes with a brief linking passage that leads to the Finale set in the tonic major key of G. The dance-like style of the Finale is strongly reminiscent of Hungarian folk-music which may have been a deliberate musical tribute from the composer to the work's dedicatee, the Hungarian-born Joseph Joachim. (In this respect, Bruch's concerto somewhat anticipates Brahms's similar Hungarian offering to the same dedicatee in the finale of his own later concerto.) The soloist enters after a few bars of orchestral preparation, with the movement's opening theme which makes a dramatic and emphatic use of multiple stopping. A transition leads to a triumphant main theme announced first by the full orchestra and then taken up by the soloist in a richly-decorated style.

Joachim, when asked to characterize the great representative violin concertos of the 19th-century – those successive and enduring masterpieces by Beethoven, Mendelssohn, Bruch and Brahms – declared that Bruch's was 'the richest and the most seductive'.

Richard Clarke

Vorwort

komponiert: 1864 bis 1868 in Köln
Uraufführung: 24. April 1866 in Koblenz, Solist: Otto von Königslöw,
unter der Leitung von Max Bruch; Erstaufführung der Neufassung:
7. Januar 1868 in Bremen, Solist: Joseph Joachim, unter der Leitung
von Max Bruch
Originalverlag: Simrock, Berlin, 1872
Orchesterbesetzung: 2 Flöten, 2 Oboen, 2 Klarinetten, 2 Fagotte –
4 Hörner, 2 Trompeten – Pauken – Streicher
Spieldauer: etwa 24 Minuten

Max Bruch (1838–1920) erhielt seine erste musikalische Ausbildung von seiner Mutter, die eine bekannte Sängerin und Musiklehrerin war. Im Jahre 1852 errang er im Alter von 14 Jahren den Preis der Frankfurter Mozartstiftung, der es ihm ermöglichte, in Köln Komposition bei Friedrich Hiller und Klavier bei Carl Reinecke zu studieren. Bruch genoss später eine bemerkenswerte Reputation sowohl als Dirigent als auch als Komponist. Er reiste durch ganz Europa und war eine Zeit lang Dirigent des Liverpool Philharmonic Orchestra; später nahm er eine ähnliche Position in Breslau an. Im Jahre 1891 wurde er dazu berufen, eine Meisterklasse für Komposition an der Musikhochschule in Berlin zu leiten.

Obwohl es nicht Bruchs einziges Instrumentalkonzert ist, so bleibt das Violinkonzert in g-Moll sein bekanntestes Stück, welches sowohl bei Interpreten als auch beim Publikum sehr beliebt ist. Die anhaltende Popularität dieses Konzertes liegt wahrscheinlich in der reizvollen Mischung aus romantischem Gefühl (besonders im *Adagio*) und virtuoser Darbietung des Soloinstruments begründet. Wie man an den Äußerungen gegenüber Simrock aus dem Jahre 1872 ablesen kann, machte sich Bruch offensichtlich sehr viele Gedanken, bis er die endgültige Form des Werkes festgelegt hatte: „Ich habe von 1864–68 mein Concert gewiß einhalb Dutzendmal wieder umgeworfen, und mit x Geigern conferirt, bevor es endlich die Form gewonnen hat, in der es nun allgemein bekannt ist und überall gespielt wird."

Der Briefwechsel zwischen Max Bruch und Joseph Joachim, der aus der Zeit der Überarbeitung des Werkes erhalten geblieben ist, gibt uns einen wertvollen Einblick in die partnerschaftliche Zusammenarbeit des Komponisten mit dem möglichen Solisten, bis hin zu Details über die Gattungsbeschreibung des Werkes und den endgültigen Titel. Bruch war sich offensichtlich nicht sicher, ob er das Werk überhaupt als Konzert bezeichnen sollte, wie wir der folgenden subtilen und verständnisvollen Antwort des großen Geigers entnehmen können: „Auf Ihre ‚Zweifel'", schreibt Joachim, „freue ich mich Ihnen schließlich zu sagen, daß ich den Titel *Concert* jedenfalls gerechtfertigt finde – für den Namen ‚Phantasie' sind namentlich die beiden letzten Sätze zu sehr und zu regelmäßig ausgebaut."

Es mag etwas überraschend und unerwartet erscheinen, dass das Konzert traditionelle Formen eher vermeidet. Der erste Satz ist ein rhapsodisches Vorspiel zum gesamten Werk und beginnt mit einem aufsteigenden, quasi improvisierten Arpeggio des Solisten. Das zweite gegensätzliche Thema in B-Dur wird auch wieder vom Solisten eingeführt. Es besteht aus einer langen kantablen Melodie, die mit einer Folge von Trillerfiguren langsam durch das Stimmregister der Violine aufsteigt. Das Werk geht dann in ein mehr oder weniger klassisches Schema der Sonatenform über. Die Themen, die bisher vorgestellt wurden, werden einer Reihe von Durchführungen unterzogen bis – anstelle einer traditionellen Reprise – die Arpeggio-Figur der Violine vom Anfang des Satzes zurückkehrt und eine Überleitung direkt in den zweiten Satz bildet, das emotionale und thematische Herzstück des Werkes.

Der mittlere *Adagio*-Satz – in der gegensätzlichen Tonart Es-Dur – beginnt mit einer sehr intensiven emotionalen Melodie in der Violine. Der Satz entfaltet eine Reihe von Themen, von denen die ersten drei vom Solisten eingeführt werden. Ein viertes Thema wird von den Hörnern und Holzbläsern angekündigt, der Solist spielt dagegen eine verzierte Triolenfigur. Das *Adagio* endet mit einer kurzen überleitenden Passage, die zum Finale hinführt, welches in der Tonart G-Dur steht. Der nahezu tänzerische Stil des Finales hat starke Anklänge an die ungarische Volksmusik, wahrscheinlich ein bewusster musikalischer Tribut des Komponisten an den in Ungarn geborenen Joseph Joachim, dem das Werk gewidmet ist. Bruchs Konzert nimmt somit in gewisser Weise Brahms' ähnlichen ungarischen Einschlag im Finale seines eigenen späteren Konzertes vorweg, welches ebenfalls Joseph Joachim gewidmet ist. Der Solist beginnt nach ein paar Takten Orchestereinleitung mit dem Eröffnungsthema des Satzes, das in dramatischer und emphatischer Art und Weise Gebrauch von Doppelgriffen macht. Eine Überleitung führt schließlich zum triumphalen Hauptthema, das zuerst vom ganzen Orchester angekündigt und dann vom Solisten übernommen und reich verziert wird.

Wenn man Joseph Joachim darum bat, die großen, bedeutenden Violinkonzerte des 19. Jahrhunderts zu beschreiben – jene aufeinander folgenden und beständigen Meisterwerke von Beethoven, Mendelssohn, Bruch und Brahms –, so erklärte er, dass Bruchs Violinkonzert „das reichste und am meisten verlockende" sei.

Richard Clarke
Übersetzung: Uta Heipp

Concerto No. 1

Max Bruch
(1838–1920)
Op. 26

I. Vorspiel
Allegro moderato

© 2007 Ernst Eulenburg Ltd, London
and Ernst Eulenburg & Co GmbH, Mainz

4

ritard.

Un poco più lento

14

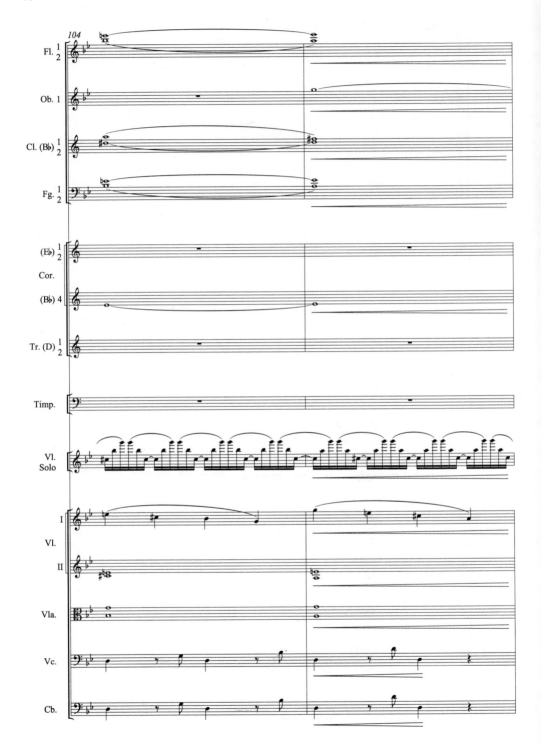

17

Un poco più vivo

EAS 118

18

19

EAS 118

20

EAS 118

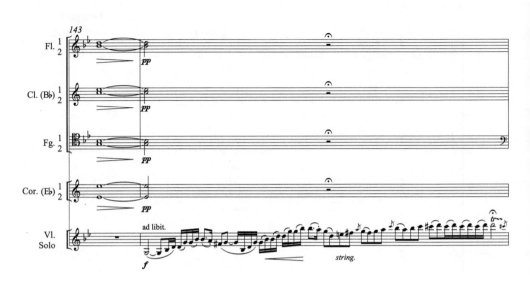

28

II. Adagio

EAS 118

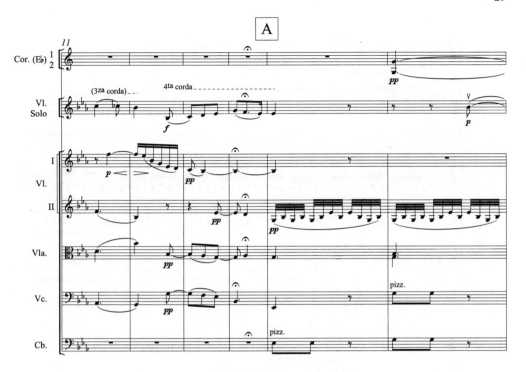

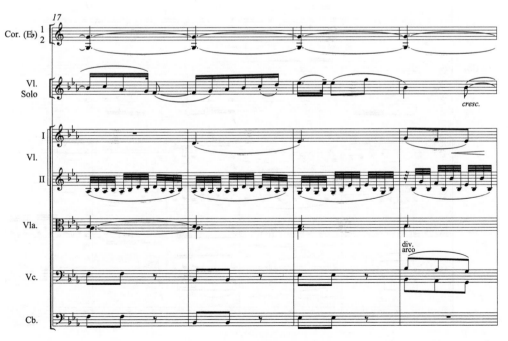

33

EAS 118

38

EAS 118

a tempo   F

G

42

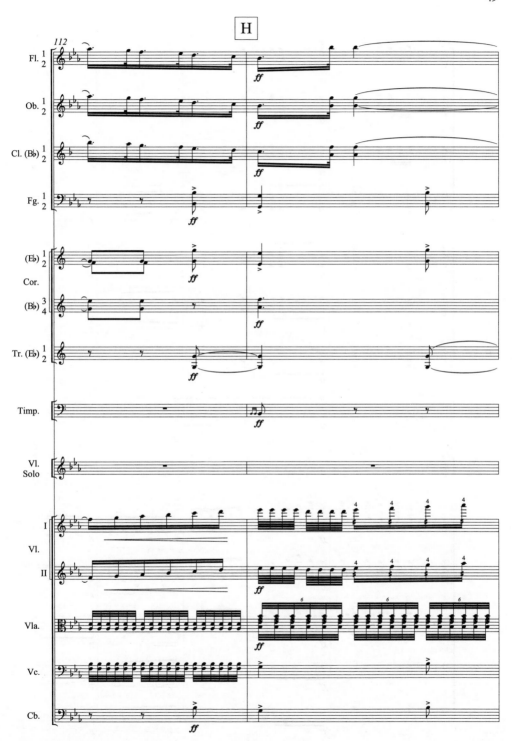

44

46

EAS 118

47

EAS 118

48

50

III. Finale
Allegro energico

56

58

EAS 118

62

64

67

EAS 118

68

poco rit.

70

EAS 118

72

EAS 118

73

EAS 118

76

78

80

84

EAS 118

EAS 118

92

L stringendo poco a poco

Presto